There once was a girl called Red Riding Hood,
who was ever so kind and always good.
One day, Red said goodbye to her mum –
Grandma was ill and had asked her to come.

She took tasty cakes
and pretty flowers

Jam

Bye!

and she said she'd be back
in about three hours.

Little Red walked through the woods, all alone,
little knowing she should have stayed at home!

A huge, hairy wolf hid behind a tree –
he wanted to eat Little Red for his tea.
He quietly **followed** her through the wood
and thought to himself,

"Oh, yes! That smells good!"

Home
Park
Grandma's house
School

The wolf raced past Red to Grandma's house,
where he tiptoed in, quiet as a mouse.

He gobbled up Grandma in one big bite –
poor Grandma was feeling too ill to fight!

The wolf dressed as Grandma and got into bed.
His big mouth watered when he saw Little Red.

Hello!

When **Red** saw the wolf, she was really **surprised!**

"Oh, Grandma!" she said,
"You have very big eyes!

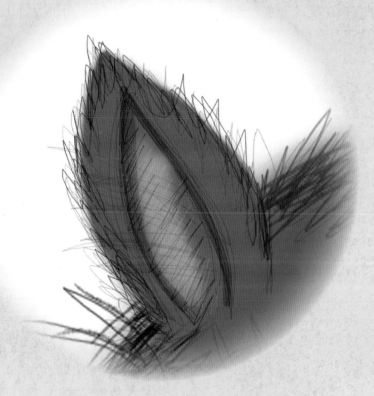

And Grandma, look at your
big, pointed ears!"
"Come close!" said the wolf,
"Don't have any fears!"

When Red moved closer,
she got such a fright –
the wolf swallowed her down
in one large bite!